A girl called Britney

A girl called Britney

A Popjustice Book
Illustrated by David Whittle

First published in Great Britain in 2006 by Friday Books
An imprint of The Friday Project Limited
83 Victoria Street, London SW1H 0HW

www.thefridayproject.co.uk
www.fridaybooks.co.uk

Text © Peter Robinson 2006
Illustrations © David Whittle 2006

ISBN – 10 1 905548 10 9
ISBN – 13 978 1 905548 10 1

British Library Cataloguing in Publication Data

A catalogue record for this book is available
from the British Library

Designed and produced by Staziker Jones
www.stazikerjones.co.uk

The Publisher's policy is to use paper
manufactured from sustainable sources

This book belongs to

_____

I am ____ years old

My favourite Britney song is _____

When I grow up, I want to be _____

Here is my autograph!

_____

This is Britney.

Britney is so lucky.

Britney is a star.

She is very famous for singing songs – because she is very good at it!

Britney likes to have babies.

This is a shame because having babies takes a lot of time, and Britney should really be spending that time making pop music.

After all, it's her job!

Britney also likes to dress up in lots of different outfits.

Once she went outside wearing just a snake.

Silly Britney bought the wrong type of boa!

Britney likes to have fun but she is also very serious about important things.

For example, when America was having an argument with another country, Britney said: "Honestly, I think we should just trust our President in every decision he makes."

She had obviously thought very hard about this so it was hard to argue!

When Britney was a little girl, she went to a very special school. The headmaster was Mickey Mouse!

Britney made lots of friends at school, including a boy called Justin and a girl called Christina.

Justin was very pretty and Christina could sing very loudly.

After Britney finished school, she wanted to be a pop singer.

She decided that she should make the best pop song in the world.

A man called Max helped her out with this!

When her first record came out, silly Britney forgot to buy any clothes so she had to wear an old school uniform as punishment.

This confused grown-ups. Ladies thought it was silly, but men did not mind.

Sometimes Justin would sleep at Britney's house. They loved each other!

Britney was not allowed to make babies with Justin because God had told her not to.

This made Britney sad because she wanted to make babies with Justin.

Or to at least practice!

After he and Britney had been special friends for a long time, Justin went away.

Perhaps if Britney had given him a hug every now and then he would not have gone away!

This made Britney very sad indeed and she cried a lot.

To cheer herself up, Britney decided to be like her hero, a girl called Madonna.

Madonna sometimes acted in films. Britney thought she would do the same.

Britney's film was called 'Crossroads'.

£3.99 *

A girl called Madonna

A Popjustice Book
Illustrated by David Whittle

*Available at all good bookshops!

At the cinema, everyone thought the film was very funny.

Unfortunately it was not supposed to be a comedy.

Britney had got her wish, though, because her film was just like Madonna's films – not very good at all!

One day Britney tried working on an aeroplane, but she got the safety instructions all wrong.

She was playing with her chest when she should have been blowing a whistle!

Because Britney likes to dress up, Britney once dressed up as if she was at a wedding, and she kissed Madonna.

So did her old friend Christina!

A girl called Missy was there too but she did not kiss Madonna.

Maybe Americans do get irony after all!

SMOOCH!

Justin saw all this happen and Britney's kiss with Madonna made him look very angry.

Perhaps he still loved Britney?

But as luck would have it, there were wedding bells just around the corner – and Britney decided to get married for real!

Except not to Justin.

But Britney enjoyed her wedding so much that a few months later she decided to have another one.

Again, not to Justin.

Britney's new husband, Kevin, was once a professional dancer.

He certainly danced his way into Britney's life very professionally!

Kevin probably did not realise it before he married Britney, but Britney had lots of money.

This meant that Kevin did not have to dance any more to make money.

Instead, he unexpectedly found that he could sit at home drinking milkshakes and smoking cigarettes!

Britney enjoyed doing this too.

After she had known Kevin for a while, Britney's belly became all swollen.

People thought this was because her heart was no longer lonely and was so full of happiness.

Actually, Britney was pregnant with a baby!

Britney was a very proud mummy.

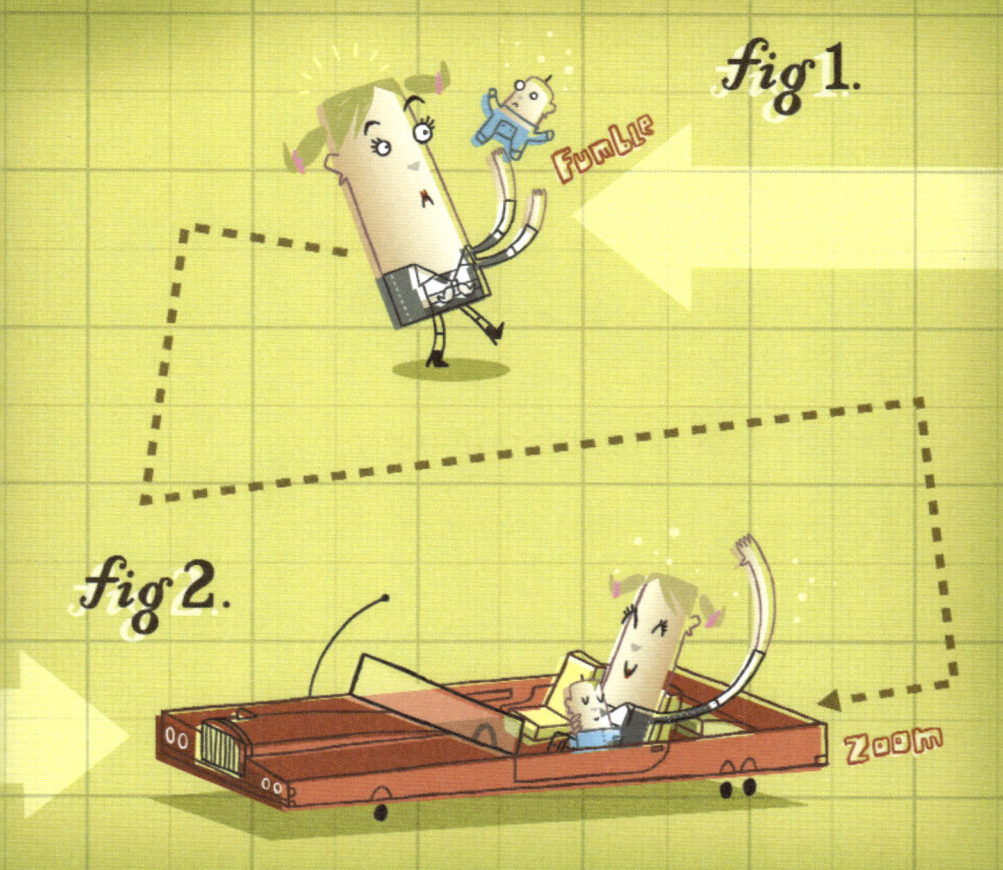

fig 1.

Fumble

fig 2.

Zoom

So that is the story of a girl called Britney.

She is a perfect popstar and a
perfect mummy.

Even Justin learned to be happy without
Britney and started to get hugs from a girl
called Cameron instead.

What a happy ending for everyone!

Britney and Justin were introduced by Mickey Mouse and became very special friends.

Cut around the edges (be careful with the scissors!) and act out scenes.

Justin: Can we have a kiss and a cuddle please?
Britney: No.
Justin: Bye!

Have fun!

pop! justice idols

Loads more Popjustice Idols are waiting to say hello to you in your local bookshop - including Robbie Williams, Britney Spears, Eminem, Pete Doherty, Michael Jackson, Elton John, Take That and Madonna!

www.popjustice.com/idols

PLUS!

THE WEBSITE!

Daily updates, podcasts, videos, downloads, pop gossip, pop stuff, pop in general... Plus get Popjustice on your mobile phone!

www.popjustice.com

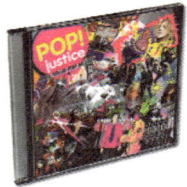

THE ALBUM!

The greatest pop album of all time, featuring AMAZING songs by AMAZING popstars, all mixed nicely together!

www.popjustice.com/album

THE CLUB NIGHT!

Two floors of unbelievable pop music, every week, in the centre of London town. We do not play stuff by Shayne Ward!

www.popjustice.com/club